GIANT PANDAS

Celebrating Bears at the Smithsonian's National Zoo

Official Commemorative Guide

BECKON BOOKS

Honoring China

Hsing-Hsing (pictured) and Ling-Ling were brought to the Zoo in 1972. Before the pandas arrived, Zoo staff knew that the pandas had been given Chinese names but did not know what they were.

熊猫

A National Legacy

THE LEGACY OF GIANT PANDAS AT THE SMITHSONIAN'S NATIONAL ZOO BEGAN IN 1972 DURING president Richard Nixon's historic visit to the People's Republic of China. Seated next to Chinese premier Zhou Enlai at a dinner in Beijing, first lady Pat Nixon mentioned her fondness for the black-and-white bears. Eager to build better relations with the United States, Zhou said, "I'll give you some."

Ling-Ling and Hsing-Hsing soon arrived at the National Zoo from China, and on April 20, 1972, Mrs. Nixon formally welcomed them to the nation's capital. The pandas became the Zoo's star attraction. Ling-Ling and Hsing-Hsing produced five cubs over the next 20 years, but sadly, none survived. The heartbreak of losing the cubs, however, spurred Zoo scientists to better understand and solve the mysteries behind giant panda reproduction.

The Zoo's research efforts continued with the next pair of pandas that came from China, Mei Xiang and Tian Tian. Since their arrival in 2000, Mei Xiang and Tian Tian have produced two surviving cubs: Tai Shan, born in 2005, and Bao Bao, born in 2013. As a part of the loan agreement with China, Tai Shan left the Zoo in 2010 to participate in a breeding program in Wolong at the China Conservation and Research Center for the Giant Panda. Bao Bao and her parents live in the Zoo's David M. Rubenstein Family Giant Panda Habitat. All of the Zoo's giant pandas have helped Zoo scientists make cutting-edge advances in giant panda care and reproductive science that will benefit panda populations in both zoos and research and breeding facilities around the world.

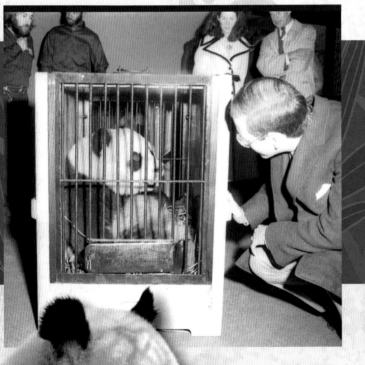

A Long Journey
Above left: Ling-Ling and Hsing-Hsing were officially presented to the Smithsonian National Zoological Park on April 20, 1972, four days after arriving from China.

Panda Care
Above: Unlike Mei Xiang and Tian Tian, Ling-Ling and Hsing-Hsing spent a lot of time together. They were managed together most of the time.

Adorable Bears
Left: Ling-Ling chews on a piece of bamboo on June 1, 1972. Theodore Reed, then park director of the National Zoo, warned visitors that the bears would "steal your heart away."

Strike a Pose
Right: Millions of visitors captured Hsing-Hsing (pictured) and Ling-Ling on camera. Hsing-Hsing lived at the Zoo for 27 years, Ling-Ling for 20.

Cub Watch
Below: Zoo staff monitored Hsing-Hsing and Ling-Ling carefully, hoping they would produce cubs. Although Ling-Ling gave birth to five cubs, none survived.

Water Play
Bottom right: Hsing-Hsing played in the water whenever he had the chance. Although it may seem unlikely, giant pandas often enjoy taking a refreshing dip.

BEHIND THE SCENES

Although people often think of Mei Xiang and Tian Tian as a couple, they're more like neighbors. They don't share physical space at the same time except when coming together to breed, but they interact as they would in the wild, vocalizing and communicating through scent markings. When rotating spaces, they'll sniff out where the other has been and scent mark those areas.

熊猫
A National Legacy

Official Welcome
Left: First lady Pat Nixon officially accepted Hsing-Hsing and Ling-Ling to the National Zoo in a ceremony that included Dillon Ripley, then director of the Smithsonian, and Chinese delegation officials.

Preparing for Her Journey
Below: Mei Xiang was born at the China Conservation and Research Center for the Giant Panda in Wolong, Sichuan province. She came to the National Zoo in 2000, when she was two years old.

SAVING THE SPECIES

The Smithsonian Conservation Biology Institute (SCBI) plays a key role in the National Zoo's global efforts to understand giant pandas and other endangered species. Headquartered in Front Royal, Virginia, with associated laboratories in Washington, DC, SCBI has one of the world's foremost biomedical research teams. It uses an integrative, cross-disciplinary approach that includes colleagues in clinical medicine, pathology, reproductive sciences, genetics, nutrition, and life and conservation sciences. The institute's goal is to find real-world solutions to conservation problems, especially those related to species' health, well-being, and survival. Among the team's achievements are pioneering technologies that have led to more consistently successful artificial insemination procedures for the giant panda, cheetah, and black-footed ferret.

熊猫

All About Pandas

AMONG THE WORLD'S MOST RECOGNIZED—BUT RAREST—ANIMALS, GIANT PANDAS LIVE IN THE mountain ranges of the Sichuan, Shanxi, and Gansu provinces in central China. Giant pandas are about the size of an American black bear, standing between two and three feet tall at the shoulder. They range from four to six feet long, weighing between 220 and 250 pounds. Until recently, it was thought that pandas spent most of their adult lives alone, with males and females meeting only during the breeding season. Yet recent studies show that small groups of pandas may share a large territory and come together other than to mate.

Pandas reach breeding maturity between four and eight years old. Females ovulate once a year in the spring for just two to three days—the only time they can conceive. This naturally slow breeding rate prevents populations in the wild from quickly recovering from illegal hunting, habitat loss, and other human-related causes of mortality.

Giant pandas are listed as endangered on the International Union for Conservation of Nature (IUCN) Red List of Threatened Species, with approximately 1,600 left in the wild. More than 375 live in zoos throughout the world and in research and breeding centers in China.

Family Matters
Above left: In the wild, female giant pandas can produce, at best, one or two young every other year. They may only successfully raise five to eight cubs in their lifetime.

Beat the Heat
Above: To help the pandas combat Washington's summer heat, the Zoo installed air conditioned grottoes and mist sprayers in their outdoor enclosures.

A Father's Legacy
Left: Tian Tian (pictured) has sired only two surviving cubs—Tai Shan and Bao Bao. Yet his father, Pan Pan, has sired 32 cubs, including seven in 1997 alone! Pan Pan was bred with many different females. A huge portion of the genes in today's captive panda population come from him.

FUN FACTS

Scientists aren't certain why giant pandas have their distinctive black-and-white coloring. Some speculate that the animals' bold contrast provides effective camouflage against their snow-dappled rocky surroundings.

A Long Life
Scientists aren't sure how long giant pandas live in the wild, but they are sure pandas live longer in zoos. Chinese scientists have reported zoo pandas as old as 35.

Straight to the Top
Right: Tai Shan, like most giant pandas, is an excellent climber. While at the National Zoo, he often took advantage of the rock and tree structures.

Cooling Off
Below: Mei Xiang is especially fond of fruitsicles. Similar to popsicles, fruitsicles are made of water and cut up fruit and are frozen to create a cold treat for the pandas on a hot day.

Let It Snow
Bottom right: The temperate forests of the pandas' native central China receive about 30 to 40 inches of rain and snow per year. Charleston, West Virginia, receives about the same amount of rain and snow—an average of 42.5 inches annually.

"MEI XIANG AND TIAN TIAN RECOGNIZE OUR VOICES. MANY VISITORS CALL OUT THEIR NAME, BUT AS SOON AS THEY HEAR ONE OF THE KEEPERS CALLING THEM, THEY MOVE TOWARD US."

—Laurie Thompson, biologist

Go Climb a Tree
Left: Giant pandas like Tai Shan are very muscular and have a strong grip that enables them to rest in trees or other high places. Although they may lose their balance occasionally, they can withstand most falls.

Nature's Gym
Below: The rocks and fallen trees at the David M. Rubenstein Family Giant Panda Habitat ensure that Bao Bao (pictured), Mei Xiang, and Tian Tian get plenty of exercise.

Making Their Mark
Bottom: Although it can be difficult to tell the Zoo's two adult pandas apart, a close examination of Mei Xiang's face shows that a pale black band runs across the bridge of her nose.

SAVING THE SPECIES

In 2012, SCBI conducted research revealing the male panda's reproductive system. It is widely known that female pandas are fertile just once a year for 24 to 72 hours. Until this study, however, no one had studied the male giant panda's reproductive capacity over time. The study found that males are reproductively viable for six or more months each year. This enables male pandas to produce sperm over a long period of time to ensure they have sperm when the brief and unpredictable female estrus cycle occurs.

BEHIND THE SCENES

The Zoo's giant pandas love snow. During the winter, the pandas can be seen rolling and tumbling down the snow-dusted hills, giving keepers and guests firsthand views of their playful and adventurous personality.

Snow Day
Giant pandas have a thick, wooly coat that keeps them warm in the cool forests of their habitat. This enables the Zoo's pandas like Tian Tian to stay in the snow for hours.

熊猫

Meet the Pandas

WHEN LING-LING AND HSING-HSING ARRIVED IN 1972, "PANDA-MONIUM" OFFICIALLY STRUCK Washington, DC. During the first four weeks the pandas were on exhibit, the number of visitors to the Zoo nearly doubled from the same period the previous year.

Panda-monium has never left the nation's capital, although much has changed. The Zoo's current panda pair, Mei Xiang and Tian Tian, and their youngest cub, Bao Bao, live in a 12,000-square-foot habitat with panda cams sponsored by Ford Motor Company Fund that broadcast their activity on the Internet. After Tai Shan was born in 2005, the Zoo offered 13,000 tickets online for visitors to get the first look. The tickets were snatched up in two hours! When Bao Bao was born in 2013, her birth was broadcast live on the Zoo's panda cams to millions of excited viewers. Tai Shan departed for China in 2010 as part of the Zoo's agreement with the China Wildlife Conservation Association. Bao Bao will most likely remain at the National Zoo until she is four years old. Then she too will leave for a breeding center in China.

First Adventure
Above left: On December 22, 2005, at nearly six months old, Tai Shan ventured outdoors for the first time. With a bit of help from his mom, Mei Xiang, he even did some climbing!

It's All Relative
Above: For many years, scientists debated whether giant pandas were more closely related to bears or raccoons or were in a group all their own. By studying the animals' DNA, researchers learned that giant pandas like Ling-Ling and Hsing-Hsing (pictured) are indeed members of the bear family.

Munch and Crunch
Left: Giant pandas have large molars and strong jaws that help them crush the tough bamboo that makes up the majority of their diet.

Ling-Ling

Whether she was swinging from a climbing structure, relaxing on a bridge, or stretching in a tree, Ling-Ling delighted Zoo visitors with her laid-back personality.

BOTH LING-LING AND HSING-HSING (PRONOUNCED Shing-Shing) were born in the wild. Their arrival at the Zoo brought high hopes for cubs. They were first brought together on May 26, 1973, when Ling-Ling went into estrus. Hsing-Hsing, however, did not seem to know what to do. It wasn't until 1983 that their first successful mating occurred. At the time, Ling-Ling was also artificially inseminated with semen from Chia Chia, a giant panda at the London Zoo. The cub didn't survive, but DNA analysis showed that the cub was Hsing-Hsing's. The pair went on to have four more cubs between 1984 and 1989, though none survived. Ling-Ling and Hsing-Hsing lived at the Zoo until they died from natural causes in 1992 and 1999, respectively.

Hsing-Hsing

Visitors often caught a glimpse of the peaceful Hsing-Hsing during his feeding times at 11:00 a.m. and 3:00 p.m.

"EVERYONE WHO MET HSING-HSING ADORED HIM. HE WAS A SWEET, GENTLE BEAR AND A GREAT AMBASSADOR FOR HIS SPECIES."

—Laurie Thompson, biologist

Mei Xiang

· · · · · · · · · · · · · · · · ·

Mei Xiang passed on her oval eye patches to her first-born cub, Tai Shan. In fact, when looking at photographs, even Zoo staff members find it difficult to tell mother and son apart.

"TIAN TIAN'S AND MEI XIANG'S PERSONALITIES ARE MARKEDLY DIFFERENT. TIAN TIAN SEEMS TO BARREL THROUGH LIFE, ALWAYS EAGER FOR WHAT IS TO COME, WHEREAS MEI XIANG IS CONSIDERABLY MORE PATIENT AND PURPOSEFUL IN HER OUTLOOK."

—Nicole MacCorkle, animal keeper

MEI XIANG (MAY SHONG) WAS BORN ON JULY 22, 1998, AT the China Conservation and Research Center for the Giant Panda in Wolong, Sichuan province. Her name means "beautiful fragrance." Mei Xiang has black hip-high "stockings" that extend up her hind legs, and the black band across her shoulders is wider in the middle than Tian Tian's. Mei Xiang has come into her own as a mother, seeming more at ease with Bao Bao than she did when Tai Shan was a cub. But like many other giant panda mothers, Mei Xiang rarely shares her favorite food items with her daughter. She has even been known to finish Bao Bao's treats!

Tian Tian

• • • • • • • • • • • • • • • • • • • •

The attention-seeking Tian Tian has two black dots that run across the bridge of his nose. He is about 30 pounds heavier than Mei Xiang, weighing 264 pounds.

TIAN TIAN (T-YEN T-YEN) WAS BORN AT THE CHINA CONSERVATION and Research Center for the Giant Panda on August 27, 1997. His name means "more and more." He has shorter black "knee socks," and the black band across his shoulders narrows in the middle. Unlike Mei Xiang's eye patches, which are oval, Tian Tian's are shaped like kidney beans. A vocal panda, Tian Tian bleats year-round to alert keepers to his need for food or attention. He also enjoys sleeping on his back while scratching his belly, a habit that his daughter, Bao Bao, mimics.

Tai Shan

● ● ● ● ● ● ● ● ● ● ● ● ● ● ● ● ●

Tai Shan is one of 25 surviving giant panda cubs born in human care in 2005. When his first health exam was conducted nearly one month after his birth, he was 12 inches long and weighed 1.82 pounds.

O N JULY 9, 2005, MEI XIANG GAVE BIRTH TO a tiny, hairless cub. In keeping with Chinese tradition, the Zoo waited 100 days to name him. The cub was named Tai Shan (tie SHON), which means "peaceful mountain." As the Zoo's first surviving cub, Tai Shan had each milestone recorded and reported to the world. He took his first step on September 22, 2005, and three consecutive steps seven days later. On June 1, 2006, Tai Shan entered the pool in his yard for the first time. He sat down without hesitation, swished his feet, and batted his toys around. Tai Shan was sent to China in 2010. He lives at the China Conservation and Research Center for the Giant Panda in Wolong.

Bao Bao

Bao Bao sometimes prefers relaxing in trees to taking part in her regular training sessions. Other times, she is a more enthusiastic participant. On those days, keepers reward her with extra praise and goodies.

MEI XIANG GAVE BIRTH TO HER SECOND SURVIVING CUB ON August 23, 2013. She was named Bao Bao (bow BOW) at a ceremony on December 1, 2013, attended by Chinese and American dignitaries. Bao Bao translates to "precious" or "treasure." Like her brother before her, Bao Bao's milestones are highlighted on the Zoo's website and panda cams. A playful cub, Bao Bao loves to find a comfy perch high in a tree and remain there until she decides to come down. She also appears to enjoy interacting with the keepers, who have used the time while she's young and inquisitive to lay the groundwork for positive reinforcement training.

"BAO BAO HAS INHERITED HER DAD'S DAREDEVIL WAYS. SHE CLIMBS EVERYTHING IN HER EXHIBIT WITHOUT FEAR. OCCASIONALLY, SHE TAKES A TUMBLE, BUT SHE JUST SHAKES IT OFF AND KEEPS REACHING NEW HEIGHTS."

—Laurie Thompson, biologist

熊猫

Panda Care

THE ZOO'S GIANT PANDAS LIVE IN THE DAVID M. RUBENSTEIN FAMILY GIANT PANDA HABITAT, AN exhibit that re-creates their rocky, lush habitat in China. Each element of the exhibit has a purpose—from helping the pandas stay cool in hot weather to giving them a place to hide when they want privacy. The outdoor enclosure includes rocks and tree structures for climbing as well as air conditioned grottoes, pools, and streams. The indoor space includes four dens, four animal enclosures, and a research exhibit where visitors can learn about the Zoo's pandas and its conservation research efforts that are helping the species survive in the wild.

Mei Xiang, Tian Tian, and Bao Bao are most active in the early morning. Bao Bao typically enters the yard around 7:30 a.m. to eat her breakfast of bamboo and explore her yard. Tian Tian is separated from both Mei Xiang and Bao Bao. Males do not interact with their cubs in the wild.

The Zoo's giant panda team includes the curator and many keepers, veterinarians, scientists, nutritionists, and trained volunteer behavior watchers. The team trains Mei Xiang and Tian Tian to participate in voluntary blood draws, pressure checks, ultrasounds, and radiographs when needed. The team has also taught the adults to receive their vaccinations in the training chute without anesthesia. Bao Bao is working up to these grown-up behaviors and already climbs onto the scale to be weighed. She's moving from the indoor to outdoor exhibit when called as well.

Daily Duties
Above left: In the wild, pandas spend much of their day resting, seeking food, and eating. Since the pandas at the Zoo do not have to hunt for food, they receive enrichment to stay mentally and physically stimulated.

Target Practice
Above: Target training is an important part of the husbandry behaviors that Tian Tian (pictured), Mei Xiang, and Bao Bao engage in on a regular basis with keepers.

Finding Their Voice
Left: Although pandas are usually quieter than other bear species, they can bleat, huff, honk, bark, and growl—especially during mating time.

BEHIND THE SCENES

Giant pandas are adept climbers, and cubs spend a great deal of time in trees. Before Bao Bao's first venture into Mei Xiang's yard, keepers "cub-proofed" the area by putting a sheet-metal guard around the trees that were off-limits for climbing and placing bales of hay around the grotto and yard to cushion any falls.

Climb to Safety
The trees at the Zoo allow cubs like Bao Bao to engage in natural behaviors. In the wild, cubs might spend their day in a tree—safe from predators—while their mother forages for bamboo.

Cub Checks

Right: The staff's goal is always to give Mei Xiang the opportunity to raise her cub on her own. However, since Mei Xiang gave birth to a cub that didn't survive in 2012, veterinary staff checked Bao Bao earlier and more often than in the past.

Trunk Show

Below: As Bao Bao became a more confident climber, she sometimes got into some precarious looking predicaments. Luckily, Mei Xiang was never far from her side.

Ready for Takeoff

Bottom right: Before Tai Shan was placed on the plane that would take him to his new home in China, he received a thorough health exam.

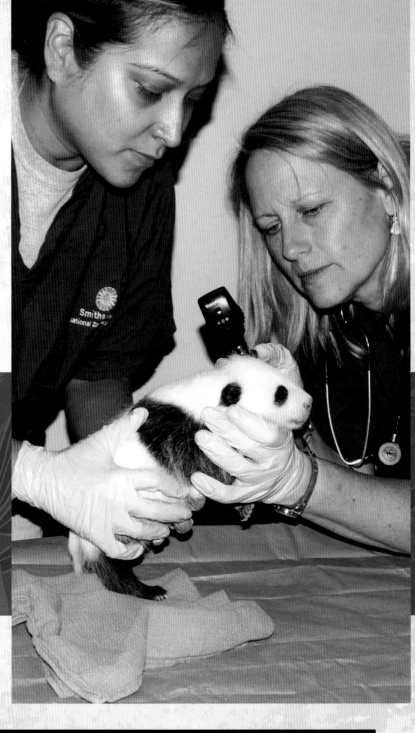

BEHIND THE SCENES

When doing a health check on a young cub, the Zoo's panda team measures its body weight, length, and width; assesses hydration; listens to its heart and lungs; and collects urine. Two to three keepers are always present, offering Mei Xiang bamboo, juice, sugarcane, honey, or water while they retrieve her cub from the den. For their safety, keepers are separated from the bears by protective bars.

熊猫
Panda Care

Eyes on You
Left: At three weeks, Bao Bao had begun to acquire the marking of an adult panda. Her eyes were starting to open, and she was crying and squealing less often.

Baby Bao Bao
Below: Bao Bao received her first veterinary exam at two days old. Like all giant panda cubs, she was pink and covered in sparse, short white hairs. Her eyes were tightly shut, and she cried loudly and often.

SAVING THE SPECIES

Panda mothers give birth to twins about 60 percent of the time. In most cases, females in the wild cannot care for both cubs, so they focus all their time and energy on the stronger cub to ensure its survival. For twins born in human care, the Zoo's Chinese colleagues have developed a method of "twin swapping." Each day, one twin receives supplemental hand-feeding in the nursery from specially trained staff while the other is fed by its mother. The next day, the cubs are swapped. This method has greatly increased the survival rates of panda twins born in breeding centers in China. In 2013, members of the National Zoo team traveled to China to observe twin swapping and receive training in other nursery care procedures.

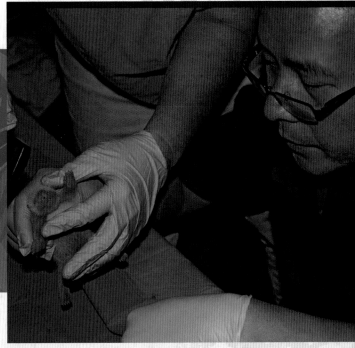

Bear Necessities
In the wild, giant pandas like Tai Shan get most of the water they need from the bamboo they eat.

BEHIND THE SCENES

The Zoo harvests about 75,000 pounds of bamboo every year, much of which feeds the pandas' giant appetites. Some of the bamboo is grown on the Zoo grounds, and some is transported from the Smithsonian Conservation Biology Institute in Front Royal, Virginia, and surrounding areas.

熊猫

A Bamboo Bonanza

Giant pandas eat almost exclusively bamboo in the wild. The pandas at the Zoo, however, have a bit more variety in their diet, feasting on bamboo supplemented with sugarcane, carrots, apples, sweet potatoes, and a special high-fiber biscuit.

Pandas have a digestive system that resembles a carnivore's. This means that much of what they eat is passed as waste. To make up for this inefficient digestion, they need to consume a large amount of food—20 to 40 pounds of bamboo each day—to receive enough nutrients. As a result, pandas spend 10 to 16 hours a day foraging and eating.

In 2001, the Zoo conducted the Giant Panda Bamboo Preference Study. During this study, Mei Xiang and Tian Tian were fed five times a day. Most meals consisted of yellow grove bamboo, fruit, vegetables, and leaf-eater biscuits, but for 18 days, the final feeding featured three different species of bamboo—arrow, black, and bissetii. When the pandas entered their enclosures in the evening, researchers recorded which type of bamboo was eaten first. In the morning, the leftovers were cleaned out of the rooms and weighed to assess how much of each type of bamboo was consumed. Mei Xiang ate about the same amount of arrow and bissetii, but Tian Tian preferred the arrow bamboo, which has large leaves and is easier to eat. Researchers believe that in the wild, giant pandas may show a similar preference for bamboo species that can be consumed quickly and efficiently.

FUN FACTS

Bamboo is high in silica and very gritty. For humans and most other animals, eating bamboo would be like chewing sand. The Zoo's gorillas and orangutans get a portion of the bamboo harvest, but they only eat the leaves. The rest they use for nesting and enrichment.

Leafy Greens
Above: Giant pandas both in the wild and at the Zoo prefer more easily digestible bamboo leaves to the tougher stems and branches.

Harvest Time
Above right: Harvesting and transporting the bamboo required to feed the pandas and other Zoo animals is a physically demanding task that takes cooperation from both the nutrition and horticulture departments.

熊猫

Extraordinary Enrichment

ENRICHMENT AND TRAINING IS AN INTEGRAL PART OF THE GIANT PANDAS' DAILY CARE. IT HELPS PANDAS demonstrate their natural behavior, adds variety to their day, gives them choices in their environment, provides physical and mental stimulation, and enhances their overall well-being. It also gives Zoo scientists the chance to study and observe panda behavior.

The Zoo uses various types of enrichment—including objects, sounds, tastes, smells, training sessions, and activities—to encourage the pandas' natural abilities and behaviors. For instance, panda keepers often vary the animals' routine by putting honey, apples, and leaf-eater biscuits inside puzzle feeders. The pandas then have to figure out how to get the treat. The keepers also make fruitsicles of frozen fruit juice and water with cut up fruit. Sometimes, the pandas are given objects like blankets, burlap bags, and boxes, but most of their toys are made of heavy-duty plastic, rubber, or bamboo since these materials can withstand their strong jaws.

The Zoo's giant pandas also take part in another enrichment activity—painting. Using modified paint-brushes with extra long handles and nontoxic finger paints, the pandas create works of art on canvases. Mei Xiang and Tian Tian seem to really enjoy this creative enrichment activity and often use the paint to "scent anoint," or rub the paint around their ears.

Having a Ball
Above: As a young cub, Bao Bao loved her pink Jolly Ball—but she was only allowed to play with it when separated from her mom, who popped the first one. Keepers didn't want either panda to accidentally ingest pieces of plastic.

Touching Base
Above right: Like the other pandas at the National Zoo, Tai Shan took part in routine husbandry training. Here, the keeper was asking Tai Shan to display body parts for visual observation. This helps keepers gain the animals' trust. The pandas can either choose to participate or walk away. If they participate, they receive a food treat!

"HUSBANDRY TRAINING IS ONE OF THE MOST IMPORTANT ENRICHMENT ACTIVITIES WE DO WITH OUR PANDAS. TEACHING THE PANDAS TO PRESENT THEIR BODY PARTS AND HOLD STILL FOR VOLUNTARY BLOOD DRAWS ALLOWS THE KEEPERS AND VETS TO PROVIDE HIGH-QUALITY CARE AND MINIMIZES STRESS ON THE BEARS."

—Marty Dearie, animal keeper

Hanging Around
Mei Xiang tends to be a bit more cautious than Tian Tian, but every so often she'll surprise keepers and guests with her treetop acrobatics.

Frozen in Time
Right: To celebrate Bao Bao's first birthday, the Zoo's nutrition department made a tiered cake from frozen, diluted apple juice and apple and pear slices. The tiers were dyed pink using beet juice.

It's in the Bag
Below: Keepers regularly put enrichment items in brown paper bags. To vary the panda's enrichment, the contents of the bags are different each time.

Panda Picassos
Bottom right: Mei Xiang (pictured) and Tian Tian seem to enjoy painting. They don't paint every day, though; the keepers want the activity to remain interesting.

BEHIND THE SCENES

In the months leading up to mating season, keepers worked with Mei Xiang and Tian Tian on behavioral training that would increase their physical stamina. Mei Xiang was trained to lie across a large log to improve her breeding posture, and Tian Tian was trained to stand tall on his hind legs to strengthen his leg muscles.

熊猫

Extraordinary Enrichment

Play Ball
Left: This enrichment activity not only stimulates Tian Tian's mind and his body, but it also gives keepers the opportunity to observe his behaviors as he engages with the ball.

Rolling Around
Below: Tian Tian proves that all a panda bear needs is some fresh powder to create his own enrichment activity—somersaulting in the snow.

Logging on to Fun
Bottom left: Mei Xiang uses her paws to manipulate a piece of wood.

"ONE OF THE FUN THINGS ABOUT ENRICHMENT IS THAT WE GET TO SEE EACH BEAR'S PERSONALITY COME OUT. THEY ALL HAVE A UNIQUE WAY OF INTERACTING WITH THE NOVEL ITEMS THAT WE OFFER THEM— FROM JOLLY BALLS TO PAINTING."

—Stacey Tabellario, animal keeper

Look at Me!
Tian Tian and Mei Xiang exhibit playful behavior during mating season.

熊猫

The Mating Game

GIANT PANDA REPRODUCTION IS A MYSTERIOUS AND CHALLENGING PHENOMENON. BEGINNING IN early winter, Zoo scientists closely observe Mei Xiang's behavior for any signs of estrus and monitor her hormone levels for a rise in estrogen. Females ovulate just once a year, usually in the late winter or early spring, and can only conceive within a few days of ovulation. When female pandas are in estrus, they become very restless and pace, pausing to scent mark—or rub their tail on surfaces—every few steps to announce to males that they are fertile. They also vocalize using low, soft bleats.

Tian Tian exhibits signs that point to the upcoming mating season, too, by "power walking," or becoming restless and patrolling his yard expectantly. When he is rotated into Mei Xiang's yard, he inspects where she has been and leaves his scent mark behind.

Although the Zoo provides every opportunity for its pandas to mate naturally, both of Mei Xiang's successful pregnancies have occurred through artificial insemination. This is standard practice in China and is done to increase the chances of fertilization and viable embryos. In 2013, Mei Xiang was artificially inseminated with semen collected from two males—the National Zoo's Tian Tian and the San Diego Zoo's Gao Gao. After Bao Bao and her stillborn twin were born, scientists at the Smithsonian Conservation Biology Institute's Center for Conservation and Evolutionary Genetics performed paternity tests using DNA samples from Mei Xiang, each of the males, and the two cubs. The results showed that Tian Tian was the father of both Bao Bao and the stillborn cub.

FUN FACTS

In the wild, male pandas must "one up" other males for breeding access to females. The placement of males' scent marks communicates the status, size, and maturity of males in the area. Males with the farthest-reaching scent markings are more likely to attract a mate.

Winter Fling
Above: Although it looks like Tian Tian and Mei Xiang are interested in one another for the long-term, once Mei Xiang is no longer in estrus, Tian Tian rebuffs her advances.

Leaving His Mark
Above right: The smell of scent markings is detectable only to pandas, but they do leave a visual clue as to where they've marked—an oily, dark brown residue.

Changing Pattern
Right: Typically, females go into estrus in late winter or early spring, as Mei Xiang (pictured) did for many years. However, from 2009 to 2011, her estrus occurred in January.

熊猫
The Mating Game

The X Factor
Right: No conclusive study indicates what starts breeding season, whether it is triggered by the longer hours of daylight and the increase in temperature, or some other environmental factor.

Successful Insemination
Below: Zoo scientists and their Chinese colleagues artificially inseminated Mei Xiang twice in 2013. In the first procedure, she was inseminated with semen from Tian Tian, in the second with semen from Gao Gao. Tian Tian was shown to be the father of both Bao Bao and the stillborn cub.

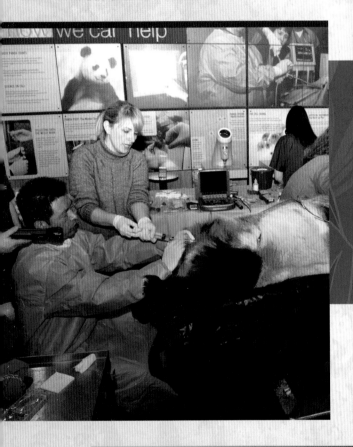

SAVING THE SPECIES

In 1990, the National Zoo collaborated with scientists from around the world to create the first giant panda studbook, a record of panda genealogy that allows scientists to keep track of births, changes in location, and deaths in the panda population in zoos throughout the world and reserves in China. By keeping extensive records, researchers ensure genetic diversity among the captive panda population. Inbreeding can pass along genetic mutations that could lead to potential health problems, so it's vital for all partners to understand a panda pair's genetic makeup before breeding the animals.

Breeding Season
Left: The Zoo gives Mei Xiang and Tian Tian every opportunity to naturally mate. When they become fatigued, however, or begin to show aggression, the keepers separate the pandas and science steps in.

Setting the Mood
Below: Before mating, the Zoo takes measures to provide optimum conditions for the pandas. For instance, automatic lighting and excessive noise are kept at a minimum after hours.

Help from Science
Bottom: Although every year Tian Tian and Mei Xiang get closer to getting it right, they have never been able to breed successfully on their own. For this reason, reproductive experts inseminate Mei Xiang artificially.

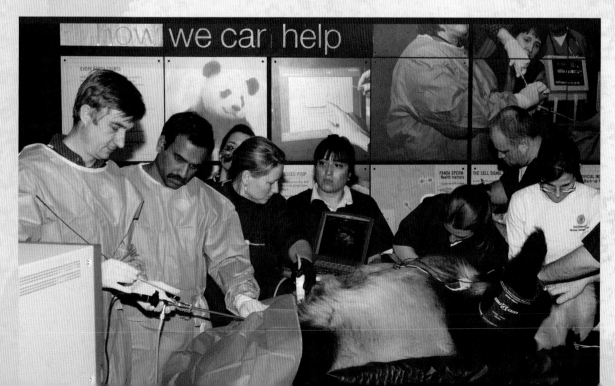

熊猫

Cub Watch

DETERMINING WHETHER A FEMALE PANDA IS PREGNANT IS NOT AN EASY TASK. BECAUSE CUBS ARE so tiny, expectant mothers don't "show" the way other animals do. In addition, pandas experience pseudopregnancy, a baffling phenomenon in which they exhibit maternal behavior and heightened progesterone levels yet never give birth.

Once Mei Xiang was artificially inseminated in 2013, the panda team monitored her behavior and analyzed the hormones in her urine. Mei Xiang also received ultrasounds twice a week. She seemed to be motivated by the pears and apples she received as positive reinforcement, as well as by the ultrasound gel. (She rubbed the gel off her belly and onto her ears after each session.)

Pandas have a gestation period between 90 and 185 days. As a cub's birth date draws near, females spend more and more time in their den. In the wild, giant pandas give birth in a small den located in large hollow conifer trees or in caves, where they make a nest of twigs and branches. At the Zoo, Mei Xiang constructed a nest of bamboo and mulberry branches. The keepers also prepared by restocking the nursery in case there were twins or a single cub that needed a little extra attention to thrive.

Den training was another important part of the Zoo's preparation. This involved getting Mei Xiang comfortable with having keepers next to her in a designated area of the den. Safety bars separated the staff from Mei Xiang but still allowed for close proximity so the team could handle and observe the cub when it arrived. From this protected area, keepers practiced with Mei Xiang by removing a prized item like a pear through the bars using modified and cushioned grabbers. Mei Xiang was praised for her cooperation and rewarded with the item at the end of each session.

0011
HOLD

08-05-05
08:24:46

Candid Camera
Above: Mei Xiang and Tai Shan share a tender moment captured on the Zoo's panda cams. Mei Xiang took to being a mother right away with Tai Shan and was an excellent, experienced mother with Bao Bao eight years later.

Picture Perfect
Above right: Zoo veterinarians and keepers train Mei Xiang to participate in ultrasounds. After each session, Mei Xiang rubs the ultrasound gel off her belly and onto her ears!

Global Ambassadors
Right: Mei Xiang's successful artificial insemination and Bao Bao's birth and subsequent growth represent decades of cooperation between scientists in China and the United States.

BEHIND THE SCENES

When Mei Xiang was pregnant with Bao Bao, the Zoo took part in a new panda pregnancy test developed by the Memphis Zoo that measured her levels of prostaglandin metabolite (fatty acid). The Memphis Zoo scientists determined that if Mei Xiang were truly pregnant, she would give birth between August 22 and August 26. If not, her pseudopregnancy would end in early September. Bao Bao was born on August 23.

FUN FACTS

Except for marsupials, a giant panda baby is the smallest mammal newborn relative to its mother's size. Pink, hairless, and blind, a cub is 1/900th the size of its mother.

Mother-Daughter Bonding
In the first few days of life, panda cubs like Bao Bao use vocalizations to communicate their needs and strengthen their relationship with their mother.

熊猫
Cub Watch

Living Color
Left: When they're about a week old, cubs develop black patches on the skin around their eyes, ears, shoulders, and legs. Black hair grows in these areas in a couple of weeks.

Watching Her Grow
Below: Although visitors could not see Bao Bao in person until she was four months old, the world watched her develop on the Zoo's high-definition panda cams.

Milk Maid
Bottom left: For the first two months of Bao Bao's life, Mei Xiang was busy keeping up with the cub's demand for her high-fat milk. Panda cubs may grow to ten times their birth weight in the first five to six weeks.

"BIRTH WATCH IS SIMULTANEOUSLY THE MOST EXCITING AND NERVE-WRACKING TIME OF ALL IN GIANT PANDA MANAGEMENT. DURING THIS TIME, THE EXPERTISE AND EFFORTS OF COUNTLESS SCIENTISTS, KEEPERS, VETERINARIANS, AND VOLUNTEERS CULMINATE IN THE HOPE THAT A LITTLE CUB WILL ARRIVE AND THRIVE."

—Becky Malinsky, animal keeper

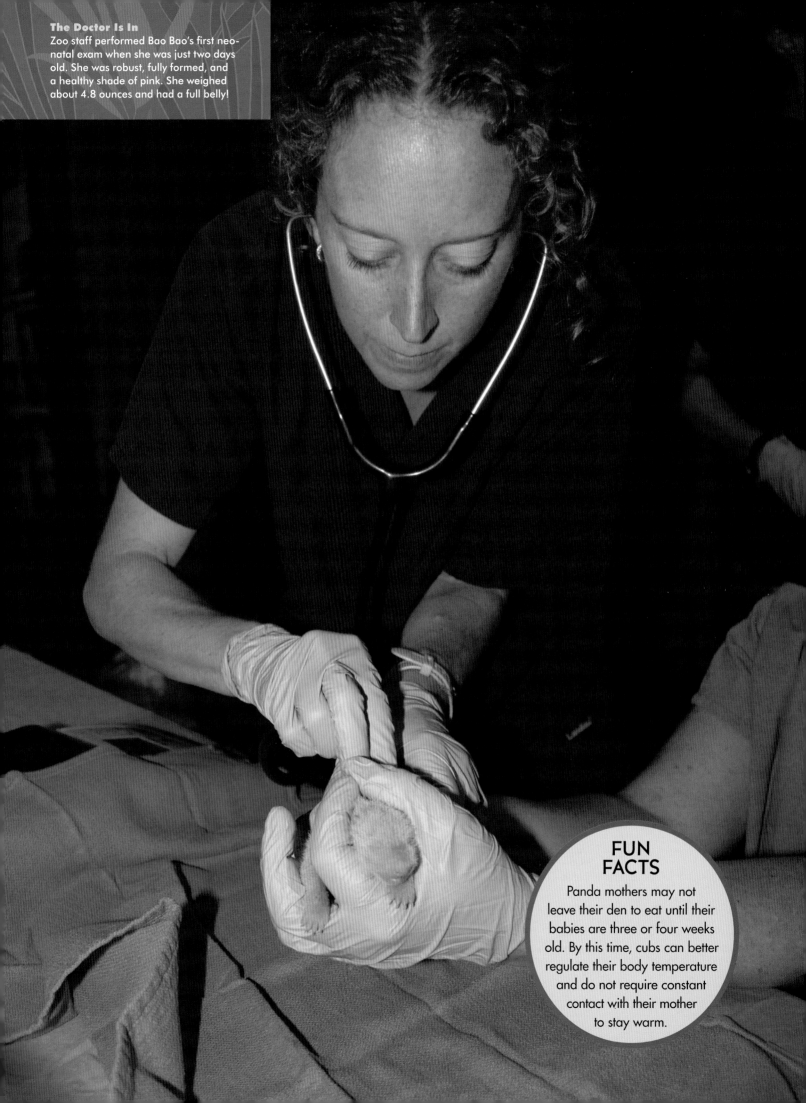

The Doctor Is In
Zoo staff performed Bao Bao's first neo-natal exam when she was just two days old. She was robust, fully formed, and a healthy shade of pink. She weighed about 4.8 ounces and had a full belly!

FUN FACTS
Panda mothers may not leave their den to eat until their babies are three or four weeks old. By this time, cubs can better regulate their body temperature and do not require constant contact with their mother to stay warm.

熊猫

Zoo Arrivals

SEVERAL WEEKS BEFORE BAO BAO'S BIRTH, THE PANDA TEAM BEGAN MONITORING MEI XIANG AROUND the clock on the Zoo's panda cams. Mei Xiang began exhibiting signs of pregnancy or pseudopregnancy around this time, such as body licking and object cradling. After Mei Xiang gave birth to Bao Bao on August 23, 2013, pregnancy watch turned into round-the-clock observation of mother and cub. Using the panda cams, the team could monitor Mei Xiang's and Bao Bao's health and safety as well as determine the necessity and frequency of cub health checks.

Newborn cubs are helpless, and it takes considerable effort on the mother's part to raise them. At birth, cubs weigh three to five ounces and are about the size of a stick of butter. Mothers spend several months denned up with their cubs, nurturing and protecting them. Giant panda cubs don't open their eyes until they are six to eight weeks old and are not mobile until three months old. At five months, cubs trot along behind their mother, mimicking her while she eats bamboo and climbs trees. While panda cubs are nutritionally weaned at one year, most are not socially weaned for up to two years. In the wild, cubs stay with their mother for 18 months to three years.

Measure for Measure
Above left: Each routine veterinary check for Bao Bao included taking measurements, listening to her heart and lungs, and looking at her eyes and ears.

The Great Outdoors
Above: As a young cub, Bao Bao followed her mom outside most days and rarely had to be carried out by keepers. She loved the yard so much, in fact, that motivating her to come back inside was sometimes challenging.

It's a . . . Girl!
Left: Since external genitalia don't develop until cubs are several months old, the best and most reliable way to determine a panda cub's sex is through DNA analysis.

Naming Ceremony
Right: Bao Bao's naming ceremony took place on December 1, 2013. Zoo director Dennis Kelly (middle) and China's ambassador to the United States Cui Tiankai (foreground) attended.

What's in a Name?
Below: Bao Bao was one of five Mandarin Chinese names that were offered to the public for online voting in November 2013.

Playtime
Bottom: Although Bao Bao loves her ball, she does not respond to it as a positive reinforcement object during target training. She prefers to be rewarded with fruitsicles!

BEHIND THE SCENES

When Bao Bao was born, Mei Xiang produced a lot of milk, so the keepers devised a method for collecting the extra. This allowed the Zoo to study the milk's nutrients and create a formula in case future cubs needed supplemental feeding. Using what they learned from Tai Shan's birth, as well as from a trip to China, the keepers created a milking station with a metal lip along the bars of Mei Xiang's den. One keeper signaled Mei Xiang to stand on her hind legs with her front paws high on the metal lip, and a second keeper collected the milk by applying light pressure to her mammaries.

熊猫
Zoo Arrivals

Mother and Son
Left: Although Tai Shan (pictured) had an incredible bond with Mei Xiang, he did not interact with his father, Tian Tian. Male pandas do not participate in raising cubs. In the wild, they may never even encounter their offspring.

Side by Side
Below: When Bao Bao first ventured outside on April 1, 2014, she was a bit hesitant, staying close to Mei Xiang's side. Soon, however, she sat in the grass with her mom to munch on a piece of bamboo.

A Royal Welcome
Bottom left: After Tai Shan was born, he received letters from around the world. He was also sent toys, soccer balls, greeting cards, and poems.

"WATCHING BAO BAO'S BIRTH LIVE ON THE HD PANDA CAMS WILL ALWAYS BE ONE OF THE HIGHLIGHTS OF MY CAREER. IT WAS EXTRAORDINARY TO HOLD HER WHEN SHE WAS ONLY TWO DAYS OLD."

—Marty Dearie, animal keeper

熊猫

The Long Journey Home

As part of the agreement with the China Wildlife Conservation Association, Tai Shan, the Zoo's first surviving giant panda cub, left Washington, DC, on February 4, 2010. Although the original agreement stipulated that Tai Shan was to return to China at the age of two, the National Zoo negotiated two extensions. These extensions allowed Zoo scientists and keepers to learn more about giant panda cubs by charting Tai Shan's development over four and a half years.

Around noon on the day of his departure, Tai Shan and his human companions—a keeper and veterinarian from the Zoo—boarded a nonstop 15-hour flight that would take them to Tai Shan's new home at Wolong's Bifengxia Panda Base in Ya'an, Sichuan province. Tai Shan was transported in a custom-made, spacious steel crate that he had been trained to enter calmly. He was not sedated for the journey and traveled well, eating bamboo and fruit in between naps. When he and his companions arrived at Bifengxia Base, they were greeted by international media and more than 100 well-wishers, including a children's dance team.

At the base, Tai Shan entered quarantine for 30 days, where he maintained a healthy appetite and explored his outdoor yard. Then he was moved to his new home in an exhibit known as Villa #5 to make his public debut. This exhibit houses 10 pandas between the ages of two and four, features an outdoor area with climbing structures, and has many trees to climb. Tai Shan is still missed at the National Zoo, but keepers, scientists, and visitors can be proud that he is fulfilling an important role in China's breeding program.

Seasoned Traveler
Above left: Throughout his journey to China, Tai Shan remained calm, munching happily on his bamboo even when bystanders at the airport crowded to catch a glimpse of him.

Crate Training
Above: Since some of Tai Shan's training had involved a squeeze cage, which prepares an animal for entering small spaces, he did not need much "crate training." He had been passing through chutes and transfer cages for years, so he was already used to small spaces.

Leaving a Legacy
Left: Tai Shan is now part of the breeding program at the Wolong Bifengxia base facility.

Let Him Eat Cake
At Tai Shan's farewell party on January 30, 2010, he enjoyed a frozen cake flavored with beet juice and pieces of fruit.

熊猫

The Long Journey Home

First Class Service
Right: Panda keeper Nicole MacCorkle traveled with Tai Shan and even joined him in the cargo area for several hours. By that point, Tai Shan had already eaten half of his produce and was ready for another feeding.

All Hands on Deck
Below: Zoo staff and FedEx representatives worked together to ensure a smooth journey for Tai Shan from the National Zoo to the tarmac in China.

Celebrity Status
Bottom right: When he arrived in China, Tai Shan had top billing on the local news.

BEHIND THE SCENES

Tai Shan was not the only panda onboard the flight on February 4, 2010. Zoo Atlanta's three-year-old giant panda, Mei Lan, was also on the flight with his human companions. Mei Lan now lives at the Chengdu Research Base of Giant Panda Breeding in Sichuan.

Fun Fanfare
Left: The people of China made signs in Tai Shan's likeness to celebrate his arrival at Bifengxia. When he left quarantine a month later, he was honored with a special ceremony.

Right at Home
Below: It didn't take Tai Shan long to warm up to his new surroundings. Less than a month after his arrival, he was responding to commands in Mandarin such as "stand up" and "sit down."

Home Sweet Habitat
Bottom left: The Bifengxia Panda Base in Ya'an, Sichuan, China, opened in 2004. It houses approximately 80 pandas, including several that came from zoos in the United States, like Tai Shan.

"Tai Shan is adaptable and confident, in part due to the many people he encountered and experiences he had at the National Zoo. He's the most amazing animal I have ever been lucky enough to work with. I am certain that Tai Shan is doing just fine in China."

—Nicole MacCorkle, animal keeper

熊猫

Preserving Their Habitat

Habitat destruction in the mountains of central China poses the biggest threat to the wild population of giant pandas. That is why conservation research in China is so important and why it's vital to have a thriving population of giant pandas in zoos and breeding centers as an insurance policy against extinction.

Although pandas once inhabited both the lowlands and the mountainous areas of China, farming, deforestation, and other human development have restricted them to the rocky terrain of the mountains. Scientists from the Zoo have conducted extensive field research and have learned a great deal about the giant panda habitat. Based on this research, they are fairly certain that wild pandas live in highly fragmented groups. Many of these groups do not have sustainable populations. To address this problem, scientists have been exploring the possibility of creating "corridors" of forests that would link isolated habitats. These corridors would provide more options for movement and mate selection. They might also assist in reintroducing captive-born pandas into the wild. Such reintroductions are a distinct possibility, as the captive population is growing. As of November 2013, there were 375 giant pandas in 72 institutions worldwide.

SAVING THE SPECIES

According to a recent study by the Smithsonian Conservation Biology Institute (SCBI), climate change is also shrinking the range of giant pandas. Using two different global climate models, the study found that a significant part of the giant panda habitat will be lost as climate change and urban development on land at lower elevations force the animals to shift to higher elevations and latitudes. By 2080, less than half of the already reduced habitat will be suitable for their survival. More protected areas must be developed that align with climate predictions.

Road to Conservation
Above left: The China Conservation and Research Center for the Giant Panda is located in Wolong, Sichuan province. The Sichuan province is also home to the golden monkey, red panda, takin, and Chinese crane.

Shrinking Habitat
Above: Giant pandas previously ranged throughout most of southern and eastern China. Fossils indicated their presence as far south as northern Vietnam and north nearly to Beijing.

熊猫

Looking Ahead

AS A LEADER IN THE CARE AND STUDY OF GIANT PANDAS, THE NATIONAL ZOO HAS WORKED FOR decades to conserve this endangered species. In 2011, the Zoo reached an agreement with the China Wildlife Conservation Association that extends Mei Xiang and Tian Tian's loan and allows the Zoo to continue to conduct research in breeding and cub behavior. The first two years of the agreement included a cooperative study involving reproductive experts from the China Conservation and Research Center for the Giant Panda in Wolong, China, and the Smithsonian Conservation Biology Institute (SCBI). This team oversaw the successful breeding of Mei Xiang and Tian Tian in 2013.

The Zoo's agreement also included a five-year science plan. This plan has specific goals that include examining the creation and impact of corridors to link fragmented habitats; determining how to restore habitats, especially those where pandas appear to be making a comeback; providing advice on giant panda reintroduction; investigating the potential impact of transmissible diseases on giant pandas and other wildlife species; and continuing research on giant panda reproduction and management.

By visiting the David M. Rubenstein Family Giant Panda Habitat, viewing the pandas online via the panda cams, or donating to the Friends of the National Zoo Giant Panda Conservation Fund, fans of these black-and-white bears are supporting conservation efforts both at the National Zoo and in China. It is the Zoo's hope that giant pandas will continue to reside in the nation's capital for many years to come.

"AT THE NATIONAL ZOO, THE WORK WE DO EVERY DAY IS PART OF OUR MISSION TO SAVE SPECIES. BY EDUCATING THE PUBLIC ON THE IMPORTANCE OF GIANT PANDA CONSERVATION, WE HOPE TO CREATE A BETTER WORLD FOR ALL ENDANGERED SPECIES. WE WANT FUTURE GENERATIONS TO ENJOY THESE ANIMALS AND SHARE IN THE INSPIRATION WE FEEL WORKING WITH THEM ON A DAILY BASIS."

—Juan Rodriguez, animal keeper

Global Partners
Above left: When Mei Xiang (pictured) went into estrus in 2013, the director of the Bifengxia Base came to assist in efforts to mate her with Tian Tian.

"Beary" Distinct
Above: Each of the pandas at the National Zoo has a distinct personality—from Mei Xiang's attentive and nurturing instincts to Tian Tian's (pictured) love for fun and adventure to Bao Bao's playful curiosity and independent spirit.

Up Close and Personal
The David M. Rubenstein Family Giant Panda Habitat gives visitors an up-close look at these endangered creatures. The Zoo hopes that guests make an emotional connection to Mei Xiang, Tian Tian, and Bao Bao—encouraging them to help save pandas in their natural habitat.

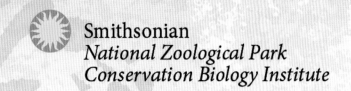

On March 2, 1889, Congress passed an act establishing the National Zoological Park in Washington, DC. Today, the Zoo has 1,800 animals from 300 species in its living collection. At the Zoo, visitors marvel at animals and learn about wildlife conservation. Zoo scientists conduct research at the Smithsonian Conservation Biology Institute and across the globe to preserve habitats and protect global biodiversity. Simply put, we save species.

3001 Connecticut Ave., NW
Washington, DC 20008
202-633-4888

Animal Care & Scientific Contributors
Brandie Smith, Senior Curator of Mammals
Laurie Thompson, Biologist
Marty Dearie, Animal Keeper
Nicole MacCorkle, Animal Keeper
Becky Malinsky, Animal Keeper
Juan Rodriguez, Animal Keeper
Stacey Tabellario, Animal Keeper
Dave Wildt, Director of the Center for Species Survival
Copper Aitken-Palmer, Chief Veterinarian of the
     Smithsonian Conservation Biology Institute
Suzan Murray, Smithsonian Global Wildlife Health

Photographers
Jessie Cohen
David Galen
Don Hurlbert
Courtney Janney
Connor Mallon
Mehgan Murphy
Abby Wood
Smithsonian Institution Archives

Special Thanks
Pamela Baker-Masson, Associate Director of
     Communications
Jennifer Zoon, Communications Specialist
Merva Crawford, Merchandise Director for Friends
     of the National Zoo
Sven Walther, Merchandise Support Specialist

Giant Pandas: Celebrating Bears at the Smithsonian's National Zoo was developed by Beckon Books in cooperation with the Smithsonian National Zoological Park. Beckon develops and publishes custom books for leading cultural attractions, corporations, and nonprofit organizations. Beckon Books is an imprint of Southwestern Publishing Group, Inc., 2451 Atrium Way, Nashville, TN 37214. Southwestern Publishing Group, Inc., is a wholly owned subsidiary of Southwestern, Inc., Nashville, Tennessee.

Christopher G. Capen, President, Beckon Books
Betsy Holt, Development Director
Monika Stout, Senior Art Director
Kristin Connelly, Managing Editor
Jennifer Frakes, Writer
Jennifer Benson, Proofreader
www.beckonbooks.com | 877-311-0155

ISBN: 978-1-935442-45-5
Printed in the United States of America
10 9 8 7 6 5 4 3 2 1

Visit the Smithsonian's National Zoo Online:
nationalzoo.si.edu

Watch the Giant Panda Cam:
nationalzoo.si.edu/Animals/WebCams/giant-panda.cfm

Support Giant Panda Conservation & Enrichment:
nationalzoo.si.edu/Support/
nationalzoo.si.edu/Support/MakeDonation/GivingTree.cfm

Stay Connected
Smithsonian's National Zoo
@NationalZoo
@SmithsonianZoo
Smithsonian's National Zoo